EST.

PILGRIM S☘UL

Creative Thinking Journal

MARTIN LAWRENCE EDITION

IF FOUND, PLEASE CONTACT

NAME: _____

PHONE: _____

EMAIL: _____

ADDRESS: _____

_____

PILGRIM SOUL

Creative Thinking Journal

MARTIN LAWRENCE EDITION

Growing up, I spent numerous hours honing in on my craft. My mother, my biggest fan, and my siblings were the best audience to have at that time. One of my High School teachers, Mrs. Henderson (Froggy), allowed me to expand this gift by giving me the last 5 minutes of class to achieve an accelerated goal. The OOOH Weeee is one of the most repeated segments from my Stand Up.
A combination of creative thinking while high and working out material became my inspiration for developing a Cannabis Creative Journal.

Enjoy with much Love,
Martin

COVER ART

"Wave Theory 005"
by Clarence James, @pvmt84

Inspired by black culture, street-art, skate culture, punk, underground youth culture, soul, R&B, and hip hop music, my artwork is an exploration of truth and self. I make abstract artwork that communicates with the subconscious and establishes a connection between individuals and universal consciousness.

– CLARENCE JAMES,
Washington DC street Artists and Painter

BUSINESS STUFF

ISBN: 978-0-578-93999-5

Pilgrim Soul books are available at a special discount when purchased for fundraising, educational use or in bulk. Special edition or book excerpts can also be created to specification. For details, contact **INFO@PILGRIMSOUL.COM**

Printed in China
First Printing Edition 2021

Pilgrim Soul
8033 Sunset Blvd Suite 454
Los Angeles Ca 90046

PILGRIMSOUL.COM

Creative Thinking is a competitive edge in so many aspects of life and work. It is about reinventing, experimenting, growing, taking risks, breaking rules, making mistakes and having fun.

— **SHAWN GOLD**,
Founder, Pilgrim Soul

How many loved your moments of glad grace,
And loved your beauty with love false or true;
But one man loved the **PILGRIM SOUL** in you,
And loved the sorrows of your changing face.

– WILLIAM BUTLER YEATS,
Nobel prize winning poet and Cannabis consumer

Your **PILGRIM SOUL** is the native, creative explorer that is born inside of everyone.

As children, creativity is the default setting. We use our senses and instinct to discover, learn, and express ourselves without the hindrance of risk, judgment, or intellectual analysis.

The purpose of this guided journal is to help you find that kid again, and to reconnect with the inquisitiveness and wonder found in childhood that differentiates us, which we often lose sight of.

Think of this as your creative exercise book. A place for you to reframe your thinking through creative challenges, thought experiments and adult coloring pages. You will heighten creative awareness, spark imagination, bring focus to creative thinking and reflect on what makes you **UNIQUELY CREATIVE**.

HOW TO USE THIS JOURNAL

CREATIVE THINKING REQUIRES YOU TO CHANGE HOW YOU THINK. MORE THAN THAT, CREATIVITY REQUIRES YOU TO CHANGE HOW YOU THINK ABOUT THINKING.

This journal is filled with creative challenges meant to spark valuable insights so often attributed to creativity, by prompting you to think in new and unique ways.

Each challenge pushes you to rethink how you see yourself and the world around you in order to uncover new possibilities and ideas.

The challenges can be done alone or with a friend. You can do them in order or open the book to a random page and start there...it is up to you. Simply follow the instructions to complete an exercise...without self-editing or second-guessing.

If you want to share your results with fellow creative journalers, There are fun hashtags at the end of each exercise. No pressure, though, **THINK OF EACH EXERCISE AS A GIFT TO YOURSELF**.

USING CANNABIS TO ENHANCE CREATIVITY

If you choose, cannabis can be a shortcut to unlocking your innate creative ability and increasing your creative output.

Cannabis has been used by artists, scientists, and thinkers for thousands of years to help provide the proper mindset to express new ideas. It allows you to live in the moment and embrace new thoughts as they come to you. People feel less inhibited on cannabis because they can relax and connect more deeply with themselves and their surroundings.

Using cannabis does not mean that all of your ideas will be great ones, but that is not the point. The point of creativity is to create. Having one great idea out of ten is better than having no ideas, or several highly inhibited ideas.

DOSAGE

If you know your optimal dosage, then proceed accordingly, but take your time. If you are unsure, start with a small amount and then slowly increase your dosage until you find a level that opens the mind. Research shows that lower doses produce more consistent results. Cannabis for creativity is meant to enhance the experience, not be the experience... let it happen quietly and gently.

THE SCIENCE BEHIND CANNABIS AND CREATIVITY

Cannabis's ability to stimulate blood flow to the brain's frontal lobe and allow neurons to fire in a more uninhibited way are just a few of the potential scientific explanations for the creative prowess that cannabis appears to bestow upon people. The frontal lobe is the base for creative, divergent thinking or thinking of multiple solutions to open-ended questions. This is also known as "thinking outside of the box."

Cannabis is also a creative maximizer in how it deactivates a specific aspect of the brain. One of the biggest inhibitors to creative ideation and divergent thinking is in judging ideas as they emerge, or convergent thinking.

There is a region in the brain called the dorsolateral prefrontal cortex that is connected to planning, inhibition, and self-censorship as well as cognitive control over emotions. Slowing it down or deactivating that area plays a role in altered states of consciousness such as daydreaming, meditation, and REM sleep (all are patterns of brain activity that can enhance the creative process). Because cannabis can suppress these functions, and allow you to focus more on imagination, ideas tend to flow more freely when using cannabis.

YOU'RE IN GOOD COMPANY

An incomplete list of writers, musicians, authors, scientists and statesmen who have used cannabis for creative inspiration and focus.

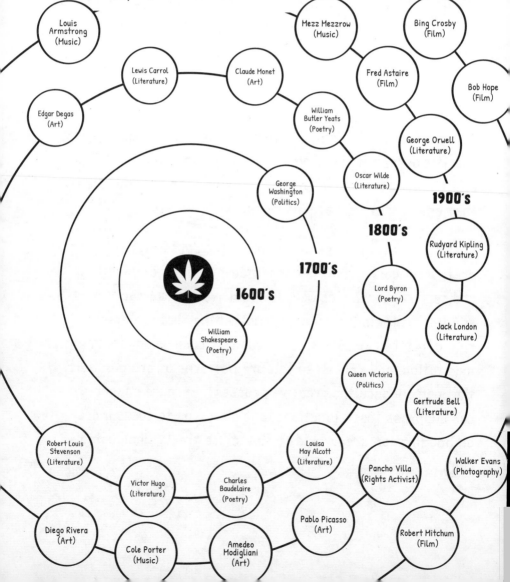

David Hockney
(Art)

Louis Armstrong
(Music)

Mezz Mezzrow
(Music)

Bing Crosby
(Film)

Lewis Carrol
(Literature)

Claude Monet
(Art)

Fred Astaire
(Film)

Bob Hope
(Film)

Edgar Degas
(Art)

William Butler Yeats
(Poetry)

George Orwell
(Literature)

George Washington
(Politics)

Oscar Wilde
(Literature)

1900's

1800's

Rudyard Kipling
(Literature)

1700's

Lord Byron
(Poetry)

1600's

Jack London
(Literature)

William Shakespeare
(Poetry)

Queen Victoria
(Politics)

Gertrude Bell
(Literature)

Robert Louis Stevenson
(Literature)

Louisa May Alcott
(Literature)

Pancho Villa
(Rights Activist)

Walker Evans
(Photography)

Victor Hugo
(Literature)

Charles Baudelaire
(Poetry)

Diego Rivera
(Art)

Pablo Picasso
(Art)

Robert Mitchum
(Film)

Cole Porter
(Music)

Amedeo Modigliani
(Art)

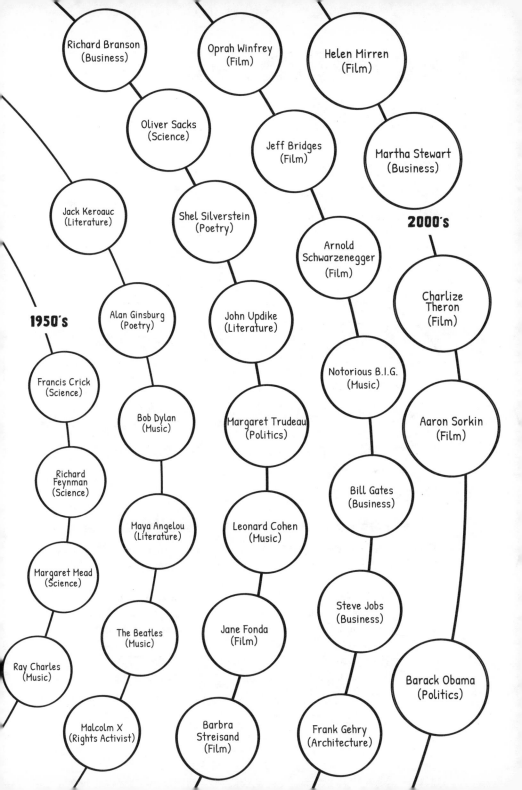

THE CREATIVE PROCESS

In the 1926 book, The Art of Thought, author Graham Wallas points to four stages of the creative process summarized here for you:

PREPARATION

Think and study on the subject from all directions.

QUALITIES:
Open-mindedness, wonder, curiosity, and a love for learning.

MANTRA:
Learn, Discover, Explore.

INCUBATION

The germination period. Step away and daydream, walk, or meditate.

QUALITIES:
Openness, patience, flexibility and unconventionality.

MANTRA:
Listen. Gaze. Let go.

ILLUMINATION

The flash of insight, revelation,
a leap of association,
or successive leaps.

QUALITIES:
Intuition, inspirational, spirituality,
embracing the Muse.

MANTRA:
Trust your instincts.

VERIFICATION

Test the idea and determine
its validity.

QUALITIES:
Truthseeker, verifier, translator.

MANTRA:
Commit. Confirm. Refine.

THE CREATIVE MINDSET

WE'VE DERIVED THESE GUIDING PRINCIPLES AS THE FOUNDATION TO UNLOCK YOUR CREATIVE POTENTIAL.

LIMIT JUDGEMENT. When using this journal, it is essential to focus on output and let ideas flow without judgment. Just see what happens and push yourself to challenge your imagination.

TAKE MORE RISKS. Creative thinking requires a willingness to fail and make mistakes. Very often the mistake is the creativity.

CHALLENGE DEFAULT THINKING. We become so accustomed to doing things in a certain way that we lose the ability to break away and think differently. Creative ideas exist in a balance between the familiar and the new.

MINIMIZE NEGATIVE THINKING. From an early age, you've learned to analyze and criticize anything new. As an adult, it becomes second nature. Don't let this hold you back.

GO WITH YOUR GUT. If you feel whimsical, then be whimsical; if irreverent, then be irreverent...but don't pressure yourself to get it right or perfect the creative experiment.

SOME GROUND RULES...

DON'T BE AFRAID TO

Make mistakes
Laugh at yourself
Stretch yourself
Enjoy the process

STAY

Open
Positive
Encouraged
Focused

AVOID

Perfection
Judgment
Self-doubt
Default thinking

IF YOU GET STUCK

Daydream
Procrastinate
Experience life and
come back.

LEFT BRAIN

Analysis

Language

Logic

Math

Reading

Reasoning

Sequence

Speaking

Timeless

Writing

RIGHT BRAIN

Art & Music

Context

Creativity

Dreams

Emotion

Feelings

Imagination

Intuition

Personality

Rhythm

Creativity actually lights up many different regions of the brain.
We use this illustration to highlight how cannabis can enhance creative characteristics.

Never be limited by other people's
limited imaginations.

-MAE JEMISON,
First black woman to travel into space

Creative Challenges

COMIC COMPOUNDS

EXERCISE: Science does it again! Researchers in the UK established a method that helped them discover the 12 funniest words in the English language. But you know what's funnier than a single silly word? Two mashed together! Pluck a word from the researchers' list and combine it with a word from one of the three other categories to make a new, ridiculous term. Then, define it. Then, repeat.

WHY?: Creativity often demands breaking established rules to make something truly unique. This is why children are so creative. They color outside the lines, play in the mud, and are notorious word maker uppers. As journalist and children's author Nicola Skinner notes, "Words are children's verbal Play-Doh, and the more words get smashed, pounded, rolled around and get glitter, peas, and sticks stuck to them, the better."

EXAMPLE:

WORD: DingoTinkle
DEFINITION: Urination while moving at high speeds, most often in a motorized vehicle or while skydiving.

WORD: AssJack
DEFINITION: A sudden bolt of inspiration that propels you from the couch and back into a long-dormant project, such as finishing a macaroni sculpture of Bill Clinton.

COMIC COMPOUNDS

Word:
Definition:

Word:
Definition:

Word:
Definition:

Word:
Definition:

Word:
Definition:

12 FUNNIEST WORDS		TOOLS	FOOD	ANIMALS
booty	waddle	plunger	pickle	skunk
tit	tinkle	hammer	broccoli	jackel
booby	bebop	jack	melon	dingo
hooter	egghead	wrench	raddish	squid
nitwit	ass	horn	parsnip	shrimp
twit	twerp	hose	lime	beaver
		clock	alfalfa	wombat

CINEMATIC SYNOPSIS

EXERCISE: You're interning at a B-movie archive. Your boss hands you a stack of dusty film canisters and tells you to watch each movie and summarize it. But you've got better things to do! Plus, he's kind of a douche. So you decide to speed things up. Going by just the title alone, write a synopsis for each movie. Try to stretch your imagination by using a range of genres. (Bonus! These are real movies, so feel free to look them up and see how they compare to your responses.)

WHY?: Learning to trust the impulses of free association is like building a launching pad for the imagination. But in this case you'll also be going a step further by activating your personal trove of collected narratives - movies watched, books read, stories heard - in order to craft brief tales of your own.

EXAMPLE:

MOVIE NAME: The Whistler

GENRE: Comedy

SYNOPSIS: Dale Moore can whistle like a songbird, though it's a gift he's always been too shy to share. But when his wife runs off with his business partner, he's in danger of losing his fried pickle truck to the bank. So Dale finally gets up the nerve to drive cross-country to the National Whistling Championship in hopes of winning prize money to save his business. With the help of his whistling and delicious fried pickles, Dale makes new friends along the way - and finds the courage share his song with the world.

CINEMATIC SYNOPSIS

MOVIE NAME:

GENRE:

SYNOPSIS:

MOVIES

Stranger on the Third Floor

The Band That Wouldn't Die

A Lady Without Passport

5 Against the House

I Used to Be Darker

Phone Call from a Stranger

Whats the Worst That Could Happen

Lady for a Day

Woman Wanted

They Drive by Night

Frisco Jenny

Captain Hurricane

A Bullet for Joey

Narrow Margin

The Bride Wore Red

Ace in the Hole

The Big Steal

The Whistler

Odd Man Out

The Dark Mirror

Pushover

Hellzapoppin'

Shockproof

CINEMATIC SYNOPSIS

MOVIE NAME:
_____

GENRE:

SYNOPSIS:

MOVIE NAME:
_____

GENRE:

SYNOPSIS:

Please share your #CinematicSummariesPS

Ride it til' the wheels fall off

— MARTIN LAWRENCE,
Comedian, Actor, Producer

LAZY INVENTOR

EXERCISE: Imagine yourself a lazy inventor who, instead of coming up with a totally new, original product, tries to do a "knock-off" version of a famous existing product. To stay legal with copyright laws, and to satisfy your own creative mind, you alter the product significantly. Your alterations, however, make for an outlandish version of the original, worthy of bemusement, scorn and ridicule. Create your bad knock off alterations of these products. Give a new name and a new purpose.

WHY?: Almost every creative idea has used the successful, proven ideas that came before as a springboard. David Burkus, management professor at Oral Roberts University, writes in Psychology Today: "The truth is, the most important rule is actually 'Combine and improve upon ideas.' Remember that there's no such thing as an original idea." Thinking up an inferior version of a well known product requires imitation, modification and humor.

EXAMPLE:

ORIGINAL PRODUCT

PRODUCT NAME: Red Bull

PURPOSE: To make the drinker more energized and awake.

DESCRIPTION: Ingredients include caffeine, taurine, glucuronolactone, sucrose and glucose, B-group vitamins, and alpine spring water.

SLOGAN: "Red Bull Gives You Wings"

NEW PRODUCT

INVENTION NAME: Brown Bear

PURPOSE: To make the drinker poop.

DESCRIPTION: Ingredients include tap water, prunes, burnt coffee, castor oil, pureed gas station burrito, spoiled yogurt drink, magnesium citrate.

SLOGAN: "Brown Bear Gives You Runs"

LAZY INVENTION
Ideas

ORIGINAL PRODUCT

PRODUCT NAME: The Roomba

PURPOSE: To automatically move around a house with no human supervision and vacuum the floor surfaces.

DESCRIPTION: A small, round, rechargeable appliance with a vacuum cleaner motor and self-propulsion.

SLOGAN: Let Robots Do Dirty Work

NEW INVENTION

INVENTION NAME:

PURPOSE:

DESCRIPTION:

SLOGAN:

LAZY INVENTION
Ideas

ORIGINAL PRODUCT

PRODUCT NAME: The Amazon Echo (Alexa)

PURPOSE: An electronic device that listens for your voice and answers questions, plays requested music and otherwise acts like a cyber age information age butler/assistant.

DESCRIPTION: A cylindrical electronic gadget with a built in microphone and speaker, and connection to the Internet.

SLOGAN: Empower your organization with Alexa.

NEW INVENTION

INVENTION NAME:

PURPOSE:

DESCRIPTION:

SLOGAN:

Please share your #LazyInventionPS

LAZY INVENTION
Ideas

ORIGINAL PRODUCT

PRODUCT NAME: The Fitbit

PURPOSE: A personal sensor to let the wearer know all about their running, walking, sleeping, heartbeat and other important physiological and exertion statistics.

DESCRIPTION: A digital watch-like device that goes on one's wrist and has sensors and computer chips to detect various biometric phenomena.

SLOGAN: Every beat counts

NEW INVENTION

INVENTION NAME:

PURPOSE:

DESCRIPTION:

SLOGAN:

LAZY INVENTION
Ideas

ORIGINAL PRODUCT

PRODUCT NAME: Drano

PURPOSE: To clear out solid blockages in pipes, such as those emanating from kitchen or bathroom sinks; or from toilets.

DESCRIPTION: A caustic chemical that burns through various substances, contained in a plastic bottle or jug.

SLOGAN: UNSTOPPABLE. You're unstoppable. And with Drano, so are your drains.

NEW INVENTION

INVENTION NAME:

PURPOSE:

DESCRIPTION:

SLOGAN:

Please share your #LazyInventionPS

The cure for boredom is curiosity.
There is no cure for curiosity.

– DOROTHY PARKER,
Poet, Writer, Critic, and Satirist

APPALLING APPS

EXERCISE: Everyone's trying to come up with the coolest new app, right? But let's face it - it's not easy to be the next Uber or Snapchat. What about something that absolutely no one wants on their phone? See if you can come up with the absolute worst apps imaginable. You'll need a good App name. What does your App do? Who is it for? Any special features? Does it solve a problem (or create one)? How do you get paid?

WHY?: To paraphrase the great sculptor Michelangelo, sometimes creating something amazing just means taking away everything that isn't what you're trying to make. Knowing what you don't want can help clear the way for greatness - with some pretty entertaining results along the way!

EXAMPLE:

APP NAME: Tele-Friend

WHAT IT DOES: It is an App for lonely people that puts you on telemarketer call lists. When you need someone to talk to, it signals telemarketers that you are ready to buy, so they ring you up and you have someone to hang out with. The paid version lets you choose the product or service.

APP NAME: Elvis Emoji

WHAT IT DOES: Replaces every emoji on your phone with tiny images of The King of Rock and Roll. For $2.99 extra, they'll also play three second clips of Elvis's music!

@creativityoncannabis

MY APPALLING
App Ideas

App Name:

What is Does:

App Name:

What is Does:

App Name:

What is Does:

MY APPALLING
App Ideas

App Name:

What is Does:

App Name:

What is Does:

App Name:

What is Does:

Please share your #AppallingAppsPS

REVISIT A PAINFUL
Experience In Your Life To Make
A Guess At What This Couple
Is Thinking?

FUTURE CLICKBAIT

EXERCISE: It's the future, and newspapers have made a comeback. It's true! They're considered ironically hip, much like today's fascination with pickling and records. Anyway, your task is to pen the headlines for a newspaper in the future. You get to fill in the date. It could be 10, 50, or a thousand years from now – it's your call. Then, fill in the main headline, as well as headlines for the sports, science/tech, food, and weather sections.

WHY?: It takes a creative leap to imagine the future. It not only requires us to picture a new, advanced (or... crumbly?) reality, but it demands we confront our own worldview in the process. Do we imagine an idealized future – where humanity has got its ducks in a row, its poops in a group? Or are we toiling amongst the rubble, grateful we have this newspaper to gobble down as post-reading sustenance? The task itself demands creative analysis and prediction, but the results provide valuable insight on our perception of contemporary life.

EXAMPLE:

DATE: November 3, 2076

MAIN HEADLINE: "President Murder-Hornet Wins Third Term as Citizens Continue to Vote Against Own Interests"

SCIENCE/TECH: "Time Travel is Here! But You Can't Afford It"

FOOD: "Thanksgiving in Pill Form Gets Mixed Reviews"

SPORTS: "Android Pitcher Throws Tenth Straight Perfect Game; Fans' Interest Wanes"

WEATHER: "High Airborne Particulate Count Promises Stunning Sunset"

@creativityoncannabis

FUTURE CLICKBAIT

DAILY ⚛ NEWS

Date:

Main Headline:

Science/Tech Headline:

Sports Headline:

Business Headline:

Entertainment Headline:

Weather Headline:

Style Headline:

Food Headline:

FUTURE CLICKBAIT

DAILY 🔬 NEWS

Date:

Main Headline:

Science/Tech Headline:

Sports Headline:

Business Headline:

Entertainment Headline:

Weather Headline:

Style Headline:

Food Headline:

Please share your #FutureHeadlinesPS

FUTURE CLICKBAIT

DAILY NEWS

Date:

Main Headline:

Science/Tech Headline:

Sports Headline:

Business Headline:

Entertainment Headline:

Weather Headline:

Style Headline:

Food Headline:

WERD ASSOCIATIONS

EXERCISE: You've heard of word associations. Well, Werd associations happen when a word is fake! A genuine phony! Match the fake nouns on the left with the definitions on the right. There's no right answers, so just rely on any associations, connotations, or sensory input the word or its sound conjures up. Draw a line connecting the word to its definition. What ever feels right to you.

"I LIKE NONSENSE, IT WAKES UP THE BRAIN CELLS."
- Dr. Seuss

WHY?: Word association has creative merits all on its own, as it asks us to quickly tap into our subconscious relationship to the terms in question. But when the word is totally fabricated, our imagination is stretched even further because we have to rely on divergent thinking, or an "outside-the-box" approach to problem solving. We have to create a new set of criteria for unpacking a word - what it sounds like, what it looks like, what it feels like. Divergent thinking stretches the imagination in order to complete the task at hand.

WERD ASSOCIATIONS

Draw a line from the word to its meaning

FREUDHAM   A fannypack made out of a small turtle shell

JABROODLE   A glowing butthole

PLARPING   A dirty window on the floor of an automobile

TOOTHASM   A pint of chocolate breast milk (2%)

GRAMPAGE   Sudden horniness after blowing up too many balloons

YARBLOOM   A sandwich made of urinal cakes and American cheese

HOZILLA   A wizard's hat used as an emergency genitalia covering

AMAGLOOP   A homosexual turkey that refuses to be labeled

BROOBAGE   A vitamin supplement intended to increase finger size

TRAGGLE   A rock formation shaped like an erect penis

PLOOPFUNK   A mirror that reflects you as your least favorite
                       cartoon character

CRINKLESPAZ   A bar brawl that leads to tender kissing

DROLLOFT   Dandruff with the shape, taste, and consistency of rice

OLGANITUDE   The need to recite well-known speeches during sex

FARKLE   A North American wildflower that looks like Rihanna

STORY SCULPTING

EXERCISE: Read through this passage from Lord of The Flies, making note of words you like or that resonate with you. Then go back and cross out what you feel are unnecessary words until you leave behind just a sentence or two that has some real, profound meaning to you. Try this with other passages in literature and share it with us.

WHY?: It's good for your creative muscles to practice chipping away, like a sculptor, to find a distinctly new idea. Often, you will find that you can best convey ideas through a simple, pared down version. Cut out the excess and make sure the heart of the matter shines through. Creative imagination often starts with uninhibited ideation, but then invariably requires editing.

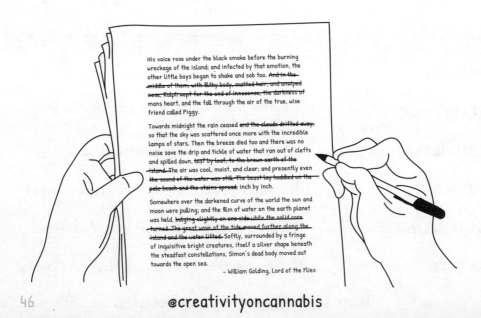

His voice rose under the black smoke before the burning wreckage of the island; and infected by that emotion, the other little boys began to shake and sob too. ~~And in the middle of them, with filthy body, matted hair, and unwiped nose, Ralph wept for the end of innocence, the darkness of~~ mans heart, and the fall through the air of the true, wise friend called Piggy.

Towards midnight the rain ceased ~~and the clouds drifted away,~~ so that the sky was scattered once more with the incredible lamps of stars. Then the breeze died too and there was no noise save the drip and tickle of water that ran out of clefts and spilled down, ~~leaf by leaf, to the brown earth of the island.~~ The air was cool, moist, and clear; and presently even ~~the sound of the water was still. The beast lay huddled on the pale beach and the stains spread,~~ inch by inch.

Somewhere over the darkened curve of the world the sun and moon were pulling; and the film of water on the earth planet was held, ~~bulging slightly on one side while the solid core turned. The great wave of the tide moved further along the island and the water lifted.~~ Softly, surrounded by a fringe of inquisitive bright creatures, itself a silver shape beneath the steadfast constellations, Simon's dead body moved out towards the open sea.

– William Golding, Lord of the Flies

@creativityoncannabis

STORY SCULPTING

"Well. . . they'll be pretty irritated about it," I said. "They really will. This is about the fourth school I've gone to." I shook my head. I shake my head quite a lot. "Boy!" I said. I also say "Boy!" quite a lot. Partly because I have a lousy vocabulary and partly because I act quite young for my age sometimes. I was sixteen then, and I'm seventeen now, and sometimes I act like I'm about thirteen. It's really ironical, because I'm six foot two and a half and I have gray hair. I really do. The one side of my head--the right side--is full of millions of gray hairs. I've had them ever since I was a kid. And yet I still act sometimes like I was only about twelve. Everybody says that, especially my father. It's partly true, too, but it isn't all true. People always think something's all true. I don't give a damn, except that I get bored sometimes when people tell me to act my age. Sometimes I act a lot older than I am--I really do--but people never notice it. People never notice anything.

Old Spencer started nodding again. He also started picking his nose. He made out like he was only pinching it, but he was really getting the old thumb right in there. I guess he thought it was all right to do because it was only me that was in the room. I didn't care, except that it's pretty disgusting to watch somebody pick their nose.

- J.D. Salinger, Catcher in The Rye

STORY SCULPTING

When lunchtime rolled around on ten first day of school,
Miss Caroline noticed that Walter Cunningham had no lunch.
She tried to loan him a quarter to buy lunch, but he was very
embarrassed and kept saying no. The class expected ME to
explain the situation to Miss Caroline, so I did. When I stood up,
she asked, "What is it, Jean Louise?" I replied, "Miss Caroline,
he's a Cunningham." But she didn't understand what I meant.
What I was trying to tell her was that the Cunninghams were
very poor farmers, but they never took charity. They never
took anything that they couldn't pay back. And since Walter
couldn't pay Miss Caroline back, he wouldn't take her money.
I remember one time when Atticus did some legal work for
Walter Cunningham's father, whose name is also Walter.

Mr. Cunningham paid my father back not with money, but with
a load of wood and a sack of hickory nuts. Miss Caroline didn't
understand me though. She thought I was being rude and making
jokes. So she told me to hold out my hand. I thought she was
going to spit in my hand because in Maycomb, kids spit in each
other's hands to seal a promise. But instead she patted my hand
3 twelve times with a ruler. All of the kids started laughing when
they realized that Miss Caroline thought she was "whipping"
me. Most kids were used to being REALLY whipped if they got in
trouble, not patted lightly with a ruler!

- Harper Lee, To Kill a Mockingbird

Please share your #StorySculptingPS

ABSURD SIGNS

EXERCISE: Look at the seemingly absurd signs on the next page and write the meaning for each. These signs don't have a standard, known purpose, but they do have the potential to express persuasive, meaningful warnings, or instructions. Even if it's preposterous, use defensible logic to your explanation of the sign's meaning.

WHY?: The act of thinking through absurdity activates the creative right brain. Though farce and absurdity are a relatively new tool in the timeline of creative humankind, they've made a powerful, indelible mark on the arts in the last couple of centuries. From Steve Martin to Andy Warhol, Absurdism taps into a primal, childlike openness, where rule-breaking and free association yield delightful and provocative results from a creative imagination.

EXAMPLE:

MEANING:

WARNING ROCKS ROLL UPHILL

ABSURD SIGNS

MEANING:

MEANING:

MEANING:

ABSURD SIGNS

Add your own absurb signs..

Please share your #AbsurdSignsPS

THOSE WHO CAN'T DO TEACH.

Those Who Can't Teach, Teach Teachers. What Can This Teacher of Teachers Not Do?

3-LINE DRAWING

EXERCISE: Start with these 3 lines Martin drew and add more lines to create something recognizable. Let your mind be open to where the pre-existing lines take you, allowing your subconscious to suggest a definite object.

WHY?: Drawing is intuitive. As children, we transfer images in our head into a set of pencil strokes, even if it doesn't resemble anything. Automatic drawing, where you are given a set of lines is a way of discovering the truth of the subconscious. By starting with lines, it helps free the psyche of guilt about what you make and that produces the most intuitive pieces. It gives you more freedom from self-censorship than you would have if you sat down to purposely write or draw using your rational consciousness.

EXAMPLE:

3-LINE DRAWING

3-LINE DRAWING

Please share your #3LineDrawingPS

3-LINE DRAWING

HUMANIZE THE PITBULL

EXERCISE: Pitbulls get a bad rap. They used to be America's darlings. In World War I, they personified what America stands for on Army recruitment posters. Companies like Buster Brown used them to advertise childrens shoes. In this exercise, let's try to humanize the Pitbull back to its original glory. See what emerges creatively by visually expressing your thoughts and feelings through decorating PitBulls with differing themes.

WHY?: Psychologists have shown that before children have advanced language, they can use drawing to express fears, joys, dreams, hopes, and nightmares. Adults have hidden thoughts that can enjoy expression through drawing too. Studies have shown that drawing can help new ideas become realized more easily while stimulating your brain's learning synapses and heightening your creative imagination.

EXAMPLE:

COWDOG

@creativityoncannabis

HUMANIZE THE PITBULL

HIPPIE DOG

PIMP DOG

Please share your #HumanizeThePitbullPS

HUMANIZE THE PITBULL

SUPERHERO DOG

PRINCESS DOG

Please share your #HumanizeThePitbullPS

HUMANIZE THE PITBULL

(Create Your Own)

Dog Name:

Dog Name:

Please share your #HumanizeThePitbullPS

RAP CHALLENGE

EXERCISE: Maybe you should write Rap songs for a living. You'll never know until you try. In this exercise, create a short rap using the 3 rhyming words and the given category. We give you 2 categories per rhyme in case you want to challenge a friend. You are welcome to re-interpret and alter the verses. "Smell"" could be smelled, smelling, smeller, you know the deal. Now show us you've got the skillz, to pay the rent & the billz!

WHY?: Freestyle rapping — in which a performer improvises a song by stringing together unrehearsed lyrics — is a highly prized skill in hip hop. Some researchers did brain scans of rappers while freestyling and found that they open up entirely new networks in the brain. What happens is that motivation, language, emotion, motor function, sensory processing, and the representation of the artists' subject experience all interact in unusual ways to create the flow state.

EXAMPLE:

YOUR RHYMES: Cereal, Bacterial, Lyrical
CHOOSE A CATEGORY: Addiction

> I'm addicted to cereal,
> It's viral and bacterial,
> When I wane multi-grain, ya know I wax lyrical.

RAP CHALLENGE

YOUR RHYMES: Burgers, Fried, Oversized
CHOOSE A CATEGORY: Streets or School

RAP CHALLENGE

YOUR RHYMES: Denial, Awhile, Style
CHOOSE A CATEGORY: Old or Young

YOUR RHYMES: Learn, Earn Concern
CHOOSE A CATEGORY: College or Highschool

Please share your #RapChallengePS

RAP CHALLENGE

YOUR RHYMES: Bong, Wrong, Song
CHOOSE A CATEGORY: East Coast or West Coast

YOUR RHYMES: Face, Chase, Place
CHOOSE A CATEGORY: Starbucks or McDonald's

URBAN INSULT DICTIONARY

EXERCISE: Ass, Bitch, Bastard...Sure they're versatile! But it's easy to get bored with the same old curse words. Plus, sometimes you don't need versatility but precision, a real sniper of a cuss to take out the enemy. Combine words from the "body parts" column and the "objects" column into brand-new curse words. Try combining in both directions. After all, asspanda and panda-ass will serve you in very different ways. Then define it and use each of your new words in a delightfully crude sentence.

BODY PARTS		OBJECTS	
Ass	Tit	Couch	Hammock
Cock	Taint	Squirrel	Umbrella
Dick	Nuts	Tuba	Caddy
Snatch	Balls	Missile	Pocket
Wang	Pub	Banana	Mule
Sack	Finger	Hobo	Buckett
Twat		Cadillac	

WHY?: In Swearing Is Good for You: The Amazing Science of Bad Language, British writer Emma Byrne explores some of the research into the benefits of cursing. Swearing unleashes the fight-or-flight response that helps us manage pain, and it can act as a substitute to actual violence. In addition, Byrne explains, swearing is an activity that actually stimulates creativity. It simultaneously triggers the emotional command center of the right brain and the language functions of the left brain.

@creativityoncannabis

URBAN INSULT
Dictionary

WORD: Cocksquirrel
DEFINITION: Referring to someone who is stingy, reluctant to part with or share cash food or drink.
SENTENCE: Don't invite that cocksquirrel to the party, he never contributes anything.

WORD:
DEFINITION:

SENTENCE:

WORD:
DEFINITION:

SENTENCE:

WORD:
DEFINITION:

SENTENCE:

WORD:
DEFINITION:

SENTENCE:

Please share your #AdultColoringPS

DOODLES I DRAW DURING
Phone Calls & Important Meetings

DOODLES I DRAW DURING

Phone Calls & Important Meetings

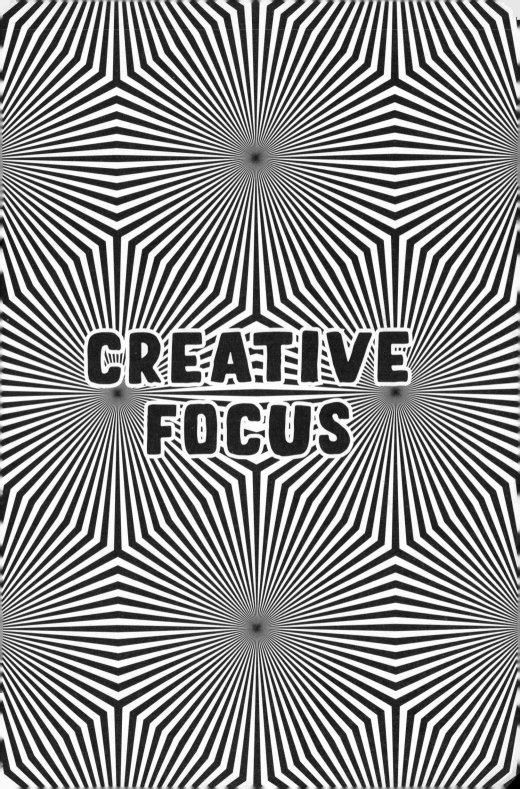

STRANGE NORMAL

EXERCISE: Use your imagination to describe the unique hypothetical circumstances that led to these situations being completely normal occurrences in our society. What kind of environment, social, religious, political, psychological, economic, biological, climactic, or other change caused these seemingly "weird" behaviors to be accepted as commonplace?

WHY?: Rod Serling, the creator of The Twilight Zone, was a master of this technique. He would radically change the framing around a situation, which affects how we judge the situation. Scientists refer to this as distal imagination, and it's crucial to groundbreaking art as well as to inventions and innovations. It activates the dorsomedial part of the brain and allows creative people to stretch their imagination to more distant futures, places, perspectives, and hypothetical realities.

EXAMPLE:

NAKED PEOPLE AT THE BANK ARE CONSIDERED NORMAL

It turns out that all those people who were allergic to gluten really weren't hypochondriacs. The genetic modification of wheat would eventually have irreversible consequences where human skin became so sensitive that to wear clothing became untenable. This would force 90% of the world's population to move within 500 miles of the equator, and result in, amongst other things, naked banking.

@creativityoncannabis

HOW COULD THIS
Be Normal?

How could walking a Peacock on a leash in a cape be normal?

Please share your #StrangeNormalPS

HOW COULD THIS
Be Normal?

How could taking a nap, on a bear in the winter, in your bathing suit be normal?

Please share your #StrangeNormalPS

You can't use up creativity.
The more you use, the more you have.

– MAYA ANGELOU,
Poet, Memoirist, Activist

BENEFIT OF A BENEFIT

EXERCISE: Answer the prompt question, then take your answer and make it the next question. Keep doing this, in a chain, to 5 levels of questions. Don't jump too radically far in any one Q&A step; leave room for gradations/links along the way to the ultimate colossal benefit. And don't stop when you think you run out of benefits. Force yourself to keep going.

WHY?: You see where we're going with this, right?
The point is to train your brain to keep digging and digging. At some point, your brain struggles. It's tempting to give up. This exercise helps you see things that are not readily apparent.
It also teaches you to see the smaller links between the more significant ideas and to draw inferences, an essential skill in making creative connections.

EXAMPLE:

WHAT'S THE BENEFIT OF USING THIS JOURNAL?
It will help me to be more creative.

WHAT'S THE BENEFIT OF BEING MORE CREATIVE?
I will differentiate me from other people.

WHAT'S THE BENEFIT OF DIFFERENTIATING FROM OTHER PEOPLE?
It will demonstrate my unique talents - creating more and better work.

WHAT'S THE BENEFIT OF MORE AND BETTER WORK?
Make more money.

WHAT'S THE BENEFIT OF MORE MONEY?
More freedom to be creative and make an impact on this world.

@creativityoncannabis

THE BENEFIT OF A
Benefit

What is the benefit of being a hypocrite?

What is the benefit of being arrogant?

THE BENEFIT OF A
Benefit

What is the benefit of having children?

What is the benefit of being popular?

Please share your #BenefitOfABenefitPS

FLOWER POWER

Please share your #AdultColoringPS

CITY SLOGANS

EXERCISE: Tourism is down in these cities, but you've got a winning solution to bring in visitors: A New Slogan! Create a city slogan in a very concise, snappy form. Share the positive (or funny) attributes of a place with the feelings attached. It can be serious, silly, whatever you like. Real examples of some state slogans include "Virginia Is For Lovers," "Maryland of Opportunity," "Vermont, Naturally." Of course, yours can be far funnier than any real one, if you like.

WHY?: Effective slogans are a perfect condensation of wit, description and enticement. Coming up with them requires apprehending diverse information and distilling down the essence in a way that "sells" the product in a split second, ideally makes people smile and simultaneously understand the value proposition and appreciate the linguistic artistry. Such an exercise involves pure creative focus.

EXAMPLE:

New York City

1. "George Washington Schlepped here"
2. "If you can make it there, you can't necessarily make it out of there"
3. " The City That Never Sweeps"

CITY SLOGANS

Detroit, Michigan

1.

2.

3.

CITY SLOGANS

Washington, D.C.

1.

2.

3.

Please share your #CitySlogansPS

CITY SLOGANS

Paris, France

1.

2.

3.

Please share your #CitySlogansPS

CELEBRITY BURGERS

EXERCISE: Many food establishments have sandwiches, burgers, omelets, etc., named after iconic celebrities, often with the ingredients of the menu item somehow reflecting the personality or tastes of the star. Come up with and describe 5 burgers named after celebrities, using logic- whether literal or vaguely associative- connecting the fame and the ingredients.

WHY?: Naming a product is a creative and even somewhat scientific act. There is a logic to a strong brand or product name. "We name to identify, symbolize, refer, describe, simplify, organize and, most importantly, to tame." writes Kyle Hildebrant and Ryan Durant of acclaimed Portland, OR branding agency OVO. "Through the act of naming, we make ties and emotional bonds with people and things."

EXAMPLE:

THE KATE MOSS ....

Patty Ingredients: A 2 oz patty, drizzled with spring water, parsley, a drop of truffle oil.

Toppings: A slather of non-dairy mayonnaise.

Bun: Served on 2 "buns" made of dried seaweed coated dust made from bee pollen.

CELEBRITY BURGERS

THE ELON MUSK

Patty Ingredients:

Toppings:

Bun:

THE MIKE TYSON

Patty Ingredients:

Toppings:

Bun:

THE RIHANNA

Patty Ingredients:

Toppings:

Bun:

THE BEYONCE

Patty Ingredients:

Toppings:

Bun:

CELEBRITY BURGERS

THE JUSTIN BIEBER ....

Patty Ingredients:

Toppings:

Bun:

THE MARTIN LAWRENCE ....

Patty Ingredients:

Toppings:

Bun:

.............................**YOUR CELEBRITY BURGER**.........................

Burger Name:
Patty Ingredients:

Toppings:

Bun:

Burger Name:
Patty Ingredients:

Toppings:

Bun:

Please sh

WHAT IS THIS
Couple Thinking About?

PASSIVE AGGRESSIVE MESSAGING

EXERCISE: People sure are annoying! Talking too loudly. Eating too loudly. Squeezing onto your full elevator. Heating leftover flounder in the office microwave. Oooooh, do they ever deserve a tongue-lashing! But that's just not allowed, is it? Luckily there's a back door to getting your point across; passive aggression. Respond to each of the prompts with a passive aggressive zinger that will shame each of these oblivious transgressors properly. Oblivious until now, that is!

WHY?: Neuroscientist Dean Burnett writes in The Guardian, "Passive-aggressive behavior is a great demonstration of the complexity of human interpersonal communication." Given the mores of polite society surrounding who can be aggressive and how and when, we've had to become more creative with the way, we wield our barbs. Sure, passive aggression can come off as dick-ish and can often be counter-productive - but there's no denying it demands problem-solving and deft language massage to wield it like a true pro.

EXAMPLE:

The neighbors in your apartment building are having very loud sex all the time. What do you rename your wifi your router to send them the message in a passive-aggressive fashion.

NEW ROUTER NAME: "She's Totally Faking It"

@creativityoncannabis

PASSIVE AGGRESSIVE
Messaging

Your nemesis at work keeps parking in your space. Their birthday card is being passed around today. Sign it in passive aggressive fashion.

BIRTHDAY MESSAGE:

Your neighbor's dog keeps pooping in your yard. Give your neighbor a passive aggressive gift that addresses this situation. Include a short note.

GIFT AND NOTE:

Please share your #PAZingersPS

PASSIVE AGGRESSIVE
Messaging

Your roommate is late with the rent, again. What song do you blast every time they come home to drive home the message?.

WELCOME SONG:

People keep wanting to pet your dog, despite your insistence not to. You knit him an adorable sweater with this passive aggressive message stitched in for these bad listeners.

SWEATER SLOGAN:

PASSIVE AGGRESSIVE
Messaging

Someone's been leering at you from across the bar for hours.
They send you a drink. You send it back and include this passive
aggressive rejection scrawled on a cocktail napkin.

NAPKIN MESSAGE:

Your neighbor is always changing right in front of the open window.
You have a passive aggressive tee shirt made for them and send it over.
What's on it?

T-SHIRT SLOGAN:

PROFILE PROJECTIONS

EXERCISE: You're dating again but it sure is weird out there. After hours of scrolling profiles, you're exhausted by the manufactured over-the-topness and troubled by the patterns you're seeing emerge. So you decide to stop reading altogether and go by image alone! Fill in the blanks to complete a profile for each of these pics as they would in your mind. Write it as the person in the pic would write it, not as the truth (whatever that is). Happy dating!

WHY?: According to findings published in Psychological Science, it only takes a 40-millisecond glance at a photo to draw conclusions about the person in it. So it makes sense that the image may also dictate the tone, content, and word choice for everything else that's included or conveniently ignored. Here you exercise creative awareness by leaning on your imagination, recalling your experiences with social media embellishment, and weaving in cultural observations to extract a complete profile from an image.

EXAMPLE:

NAME: Sebastian

HEADLINE: Live Fast, Die Sexy

LOOKING FOR: A leggy heiress to rev my engine! 8's and up only, please.

HOBBIES/INTERESTS: Making the ladies swoon. Working on my beats. Dominating the stock market.

@creativityoncannabis

PROFILE PROJECTIONS

NAME:

HEADLINE:

LOOKING FOR:

HOBBIES/INTERESTS:

NAME:

HEADLINE:

LOOKING FOR:

HOBBIES/INTERESTS:

NAME:

HEADLINE:

LOOKING FOR:

HOBBIES/INTERESTS:

PROFILE PROJECTIONS

NAME:

HEADLINE:

LOOKING FOR:

HOBBIES/INTERESTS:

NAME:

HEADLINE:

LOOKING FOR:

HOBBIES/INTERESTS:

NAME:

HEADLINE:

LOOKING FOR:

HOBBIES/INTERESTS:

Please share your #ProfileProjectionsPS

The question is not whether we will be extremists, but what kind of extremists we will be... The nation and the world are in dire need of creative extremists.

– MARTIN LUTHER KING, JR.
Leader, American Civil Rights Movement

MICRO VILLAINS

EXERCISE: There sure are a lot of people on this planet! As such, our day-to-day lives are rife with pet peeve perpetrators. People who are a little too close, a little too loud, and operate in a self-first bubble. Let's call them Micro Villains! And like any good villain in books or movies, they need fleshing out. Choose four offenders from the following list - or add your own! Give each one a villainous label and a fitting punishment (such as a task to perform or a sign to wear).

WHY?: Pet peeves perpetrators often take up more of our conscious mind than they deserve. We stew in these slights, replaying them amid the fumes of indignation. In this exercise, we harness that energy as fuel for creative inspiration. You gain power over these slights with positive, constructive action. Neuroscientist Matthew Lieberman showed that when we put negative feelings into words, the activity in our Amygdala - the part of your brain associated emotion response - is optimized for mental and physical health.

EXAMPLE:

Crime: People who walk too close behind you
Name: AssCaddy
Punishment:
Spend a week in a giant inflatable hamster bubble to learn proper personal spacing.

@creativityoncannabis

MICRO VILLAINS

Crime:
Name:
Punishment:

Crime:
Name:
Punishment:

Crime:
Name:
Punishment:

Crime:
Name:
Punishment:

PEOPLE WHO...

Take a phone call at the gym...
Constantly Name drop...
Pee on your toilet seat...
Take up two parking spots...
Constantly Humblebrag...

Always talk about how busy they are...
Wait til they get to cashier to look at a menu...
Go into the express line with too many items...
Wear too much perfume or cologne...
Look at their phone while talking to you...
Start a sentence with "no offense"...

Please share your #MicroVillainsPS

TIME NARC

EXERCISE: It's the near future. You're a time-traveling narc. Strait-laced. A real square. (the complete opposite of you, clearly) Your chief needs a pure sample of a particular batch of cannabis in order to identify some recently-seized evidence. She gives you the details: The strain originated with a late 60s SoCal folk-rock band called JoJo and the Snowbirds. They also happen to be surfers. You don't surf or play an instrument. But you'll have only one day to infiltrate the scene and get the band's singer/shaman, JoJo Snowbird, to give you a bag of his home-grown herb before the time portal closes. You step through. And, a second later, you're back with the goods! Type up your report for the chief.

> **SOME HELPFUL NARC HINTS FROM THE FBI:**
> Fit in with the way you look. Make them feel at ease. Make it about them. Validate them, offer a gift, ask for help, ask open ended questions.

WHY?: Imagining situations and circumstances in another time or era demands that you flex your imagination. Time travel has been the foundation for a range of innovative and delightful creative works from Back to the Future to The Terminator to the Bill & Ted movies. This particular kind of fish-out-of-water tale is fertile ground for both quirky conflict and shrewd cultural analysis to bloom. And it requires you to lean on your imagination in order to juggle multiple contexts while solving a problem.

@creativityoncannabis

TIME NARC

CASE NUMBER: **DATE:**

OFFICER: **PREPARED BY:**

INCIDENT:

DETAIL OF EVENT:

ACTION TAKEN:

WOKE WORD SEARCH

Circle the people that it's still OK to joke about.
Share date_____ and time_____ for context

HILLBILLYS	FRAT BOYS
SCIENTOLOGISTS	HOARDERS
DADS	INFLUENCERS
AMISH	HUMBLE BRAGGERS
CROSSFITTERS	ROLLERBLADERS
EQUESTRIANS	CAT LADIES
POLITICIANS	HORNY SENIORS
REDDITORS	THE DUTCH
FLAT-EARTHERS	FLORIDA MAN
BILLIONAIRES	KARENS
BALD MEN	QANON
SHORT SELLERS	CRITICS

```
T  R  Q  V  S  F  L  O  R  I  D  A  M  A  N
W  H  O  H  N  O  N  A  Q  W  R  N  J  S  F
N  T  U  L  Y  T  G  O  P  Z  S  I  G  Y  L
U  P  H  M  L  X  H  A  T  D  O  Y  O  L  V
C  S  O  Q  B  E  Z  E  M  Q  K  N  S  L  U
R  E  R  F  H  L  R  O  D  I  N  X  M  I  O
O  R  N  E  Z  W  E  B  C  U  S  I  F  B  S
S  I  Y  N  H  S  M  B  L  B  T  H  V  L  C
S  A  S  E  G  T  Y  V  R  A  N  C  Y  L  I
F  N  E  M  G  R  R  O  C  A  D  Y  H  I  T
I  O  N  D  Q  X  D  A  B  Q  G  E  Y  H  I
T  I  I  L  R  E  A  Q  E  T  B  G  R  A  R
T  L  O  A  K  X  D  Z  J  T  A  O  E  S  C
E  L  R  B  S  N  S  X  M  H  A  R  I  R  U
R  I  S  J  Q  W  I  H  J  B  S  L  F  S  S
S  B  W  O  B  J  S  F  Q  O  K  F  Y  C
P  O  L  I  T  I  C  I  A  N  S  I  N  S  P
S  N  E  R  A  K  B  C  A  K  Y  J  Q  T  S
G  S  C  I  E  N  T  O  L  O  G  I  S  T  S
F  X  S  S  E  I  D  A  L  T  A  C  U  W  P
V  A  I  B  H  R  E  D  D  I  T  O  R  S  F
X  E  H  O  A  R  D  E  R  S  D  G  U  P  A
C  E  H  V  E  Q  U  E  S  T  R  I  A  N  S
M  P  G  W  I  N  F  L  U  E  N  C  E  R  S
E  U  G  S  R  E  L  L  E  S  T  R  O  H  S
```

Please share your #WokeWordSearchPS

ADULTING AVOIDANCE

EXERCISE: You can't avoid the avalanche of adulthood. Everyone has to grow up sometime. But what you CAN do is make the transition with some goddamn dignity! Fill in the blanks to make a list of what you see as the reddest of red flags raised when people topple from adolescence. Consider it a list's-worth of advice for not turning into your parents or other fogies that were impaled by these daggers of lameness, seemingly all at once. It might help to consider the things your parents or other adults have done that made you cringe like you just took down a barrel of lemons.

WHY?: When we think of symbols, objects such as eagles, broken chains, or bodies of water often pop to mind. But actions can be symbolic, too. Coming up with symbolic actions that might represent a life transition demands a great deal of self-reflection, cultural analysis, and creativity. After all, you need to scrutinize your own experiences and the behavior of larger society and simmer them down to a group of emblematic choices. All while trying to get "Jack & Diane" out of your head!

EXAMPLE:

Never date someone just because they _wear pajamas to bed._

Never pass on a fun activity because the _local news will be on soon._

Never take a personal day from work to _catch up on laundry._

Never ask this at a restaurant _"This Groupon has expired, but will you still honor it?"_

@creativityoncannabis

ADULTING AVOIDANCE

Never date someone just because they _____

_____

Never pass on a fun activity because _____

_____

Never take a personal day from work to _____

_____

Never wear these three things _____

_____

Never eat at this restaurant _____

_____

Never ask this at a restaurant _____

_____

ADULTING AVOIDANCE

Never listen to these three bands/musicians or songs _____
_____

Never offer this advice _____
_____

Never buy this car _____
_____

Never donate money to _____
_____

Never purchase this for your home _____
_____

Never buy this food at the store _____
_____

Please share your #AdultingAvoidancePS

Never buy this beverage at the store _____

_____

Add your own adult avoidance rules...

6-WORD BIOGRAPHIES

EXERCISE: Let's play with brevity. For this exercise, create a biography in just six words. You can do it. Focus on the essence of the narrative. Really focus on the essence of your subjects - the traits or milestones that truly, in your mind, define them. Try to write each 6-word bio as a story, not just a "timeline" catalogue of events.

WHY?: We often perceive of creativity as building something. But just as often it involves thoughtful elimination, chiseling away at the marble to reveal the most perfect iteration of the sculpture inside. Ernest Hemingway was one of many writers who created a six-word story as an example of concise and creative storytelling. "For sale: Baby shoes. Never worn." When you boil down the ingredients, you gain intensity, an exercise that captures the essence of a creative focus.

EXAMPLE:

THOMAS EDISON:
Lit the world with one ear.

STEPHEN COLBERT:
He thought it was funny enough.

SIX WORD BIOGRAPHIES

BRUCE LEE:

MUHAMAD ALI:

MARK ZUCKERBERG:

TUPAC SHAKUR:

SHENENEH JENKINS:

SIX WORD BIOGRAPHIES

GEORGE WASHINGTON:

WICKED WITCH OF THE WEST:

KANYE WEST:

TAYLOR SWIFT:

SERENA WILLIAMS:

Please share your #6WordBiographiesPS

Please share your #AdultColoringPS

STOCK PHOTO SUBTEXT

EXERCISE: What are these people in stock photos really thinking? Take into account all of the things that can impact what they say and what they do. Do they have a secret? What external pressures are they facing? What is their mission? This will help you write their words and behavior with the underlying subtext driving the plot in this room. You can even look at it front he perspective of the model who showed up to be in this stock photo photoshoot.

WHY?: The subtext is the implicit meaning of a text. It gives the reader information about characters, plot, and the story's context as a whole. Great fiction writers and even non-fiction writers weave subtext through their work to communicate an underlying emotion and motives. It makes their prose richer and their dialogue more nuanced.

@creativityoncannabis

FILL IN THE
Thought Bubbles To Make This Office Stock Photo More Honest

FILL IN THE
Thought Bubbles To Make this Office Stock Photo More Honest

Please share your #StockPhotoSubtextPS

FILL IN THE

Thought Bubbles To Make These
Salad Eaters Stock Photos More Honest

BAD BABY NAMES

EXERCISE: Names are like brands on humans beings. They can determine how people are treated and who they become as adults. For this exercise, come up with the worst baby name you can in each of the given categories. Maybe it's just the sound of the word that's unappealing, or perhaps it's the weird or troubling connotations it implies. For consistency, imagine the baby's last name is "Smith." And feel free to change the spelling of your names to make them extra-obnoxious ("k" for "c," etc.).
Then share how they might turn out as adults, based on the name.

WHY?: Nominative determinism is the hypothesis that people gravitate towards areas of work that fit their names. In a study of 1990 census data, researchers found that Dentists' top male and female names were Dennis and Denise respectively. Shaping perceptions through naming demands several creative and analytical skills. First you empathize with expectations, then you need to use your creative and cultural awareness to disrupt them. Then you employ your linguistic chops to find the words that sound and feel just right (or, in this case... wrong!).

EXAMPLE:

> **APPETIZER:** Kalamari Smith
>
> **JOB, QUIRKS, PERSONALITY:** Highly extroverted manager of a seafood restaurant, excellent swimmer, loves socializing and meeting new people. Has a special connection with animals and illegible handwriting.

BAD BABY NAMES

Eleven new "Smith" babies have just been delivered and you're in a rush to name them all. Give them the worst names you can think of in each of the following categories. Share some insights into how this might affect who they become as an adult...

A Country:
Job, Quirks, Personality:

A Marine Animal:
Job, Quirks, Personality:

Insect:
Job, Quirks, Personality:

BAD BABY NAMES

Appetizer:
Job, Quirks, Personality:

Dessert:
Job, Quirks, Personality:

Spice:
Job, Quirks, Personality:

Tree/plant:
Job, Quirks, Personality:

Please share your #BadBabyNamesPS

BAD BABY NAMES

Occupation:
Job, Quirks, Personality:

Tool:
Job, Quirks, Personality:

Beverage:
Job, Quirks, Personality:

Article of Clothing:
Job, Quirks, Personality:

DOODLES I DRAW DURING
Phone Calls & Important Meetings

DOODLES I DRAW DURING
Phone Calls & Important Meetings

BETWEEN THE LINES

EXERCISE: Consider the interactions where you've encountered these phrases, or imagine the scenario. They never mean what they mean. Write your subtext translation next to each stock conversational phrase. For added entertainment, spice them up with your own personal brand of sarcasm or tailor them to your current home or work context.

WHY?: The subtext is often more creative than the text. Ernest Hemingway's famous "Iceberg Principle" is based on the idea that each character on the page is only 10% of who they are; the rest exists in the reader's mind. Using subtext lurking beneath the surface is a creative awareness technique that allows you to tell part of the story, which the reader intuitively understands. Being aware of subtext can also prompt you to use more dynamic and intentional language.

EXAMPLE:

"THANKS FOR YOUR FEEDBACK, I'LL BE SURE TO KEEP THAT IN MIND."
Translation: "That idea is just awful. Honestly, if I wanted terrible advice I'd go hang out outside the free clinic."

@creativityoncannabis

BETWEEN THE LINES

"Thank you in advance."
Translation: _____

"I wanted to follow up…"
Translation: _____

"Let me know if you need anything else"
Translation: _____

"I'm a little confused…"
Translation: _____

"Thanks for your feedback, I'll be sure to keep that in mind."
Translation: _____

"I'll let you take it from here."
Translation: _____

"Per my last email."
Translation: _____

"Thanks for looping me in."
Translation: _____

"In the future, if you could…"
Translation: _____

"Quick question"
Translation: _____

SUBJECTIVE MAP

EXERCISE: Create a handwritten map of an imaginary neighborhood or planned community, with an overlay showing destinations and amenities relevant to a specific group, such as Hipsters, Boring People, Hypochondriacs, Narcissists, Narcoleptics, your dog, you pick.

WHY?: According to National Geographic, spatial thinking is one of the most critical formative mental skills, one that's required for interaction with the world. Spatial thinking involves visualizing, interpreting, and reasoning, using location, distance, direction, and space. This exercise, combining mapping skills with sociological and anthropological observation, uses both the scientific left brain and creative right brain. It fosters creative awareness while also helping us to realize our own social biases.

Man's Man Neighborhood Map

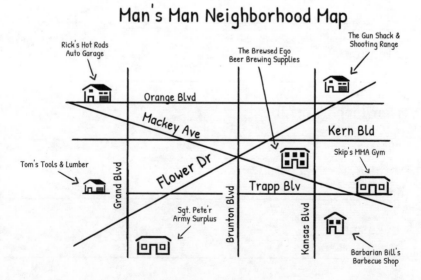

@creativityoncannabis

PLANNED COMMUNITY

for:

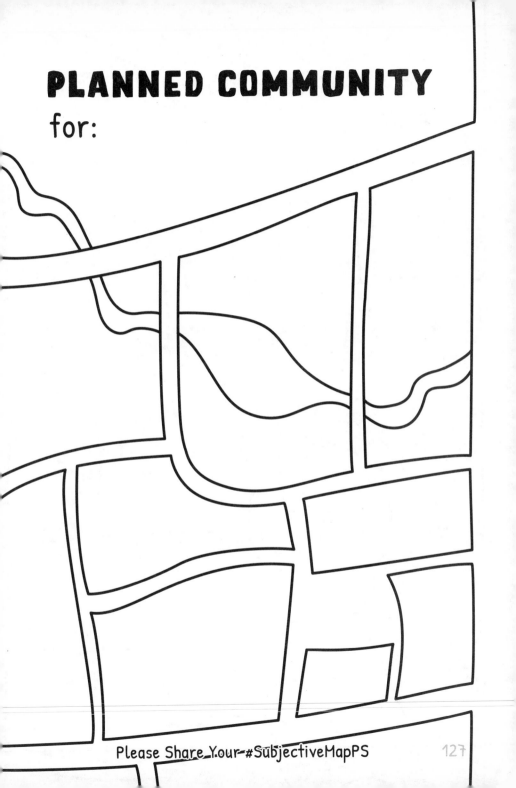

PLANNED COMMUNITY
for:

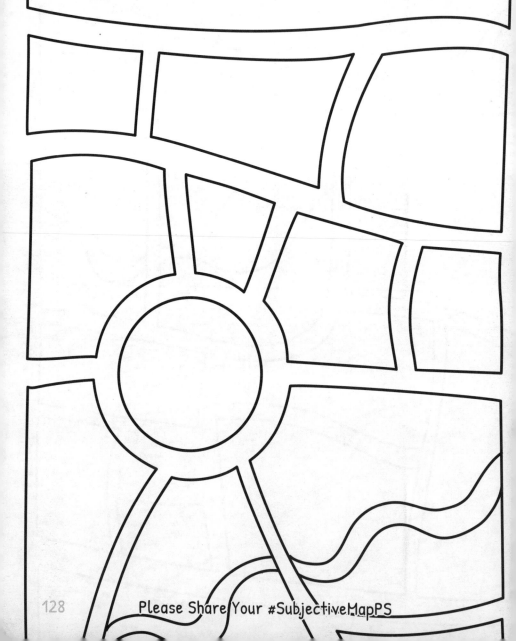

Please Share Your #SubjectiveMapPS

THE CREATIVE PROCESS

1. This is awesome

2. This is tricky

3. This is shit

4. I am shit

5. This might be ok

6. This is awesome

PENMANSHIP PERSONALITY

EXERCISE: Write this note: "Hello! I stopped by. How are you?" over again, using the handwriting of various types of people. Try to capture the personality and mentality of each kind of person with your handwriting, and make them all really distinct. Feel free to utilize very different sizes, curvatures, neatness/messiness, dots/crosses, or whatever creative elements come to mind regarding the letters.

WHY?: Graphology, the science of analyzing handwriting for personality traits, has been around since the ancient Greeks. It is used today in criminology, medical science, and even human resources. Small details in someone's handwriting can reveal up to 5,000 personality traits. Tapping into the correlation between handwriting and inner personality, and imagining how others may write, combines empathy and artistry for a powerful exercise in creative focus.

PENMANSHIP
Personality

Hello! I stopped by. How are you?

A Rap artists from the early 1980's

HELLO! I STOPPED BY. HOW are YOU?

Rural Guy Who Likes Hunting, Trucks & Beer

Professional Basketball Player

High School Janitor

PENMANSHIP
Personality

Hello! I stopped by. How are you?

A Grade School Bully

A Bird Watcher

A Graffiti Artist

A Serial Killer

Please Share Your #PenmanshipPS

SNARKY COMMENTS

EXERCISE: Imagine you live in your mom's basement and spend your days writing snarky comments from your anonymous Instagram account. What kind of negative comments can you say about these commonly loved subjects?

WHY?: A study from the Harvard Business School suggests that blurting out sarcastic remarks - and listening to them - may increase one's ability to think creatively and abstractly. Sarcasm increases creativity for both expressers and recipients. Because you have to peel back the layers of the satirical remarks, your brain forces itself to analyze and interpret different possible meanings behind the comments - increasing ingenuity and creative problem-solving skills.

WHAT'S THERE TO BE CYNICAL ABOUT?

WHAT'S THERE TO BE CYNICAL ABOUT?

Please share your #SnarkyCommentsPS

WHAT'S THERE TO BE CYNICAL ABOUT?

CreativityOnCannabis

1,020,937 likes

BEAUTIFUL TREES
#SnarkyComments

RIGHTEOUS RESIGNATIONS

EXERCISE: It's nobody's dream job, and it's time to resign. This last incident - emblematic of the whole lousy situation - You can't take this happening one more time. Fill in the blanks to compose resignation letters where you stick it to your no-good boss and make way for better things.

WHY?: Creativity demands we pay attention to the world, especially those things that go unnoticed. After all, it is in those places or situations that authentic learning or discovery can occur. This exercise challenges you to peek under the surface of professions you may have only considered superficially - It demands empathy and creative focus to close a gap in understanding.

EXAMPLE:

BIRTHDAY CLOWN

Look, for years I've been one of the top ___Birthday Clowns___ _____ you've got. But I'm sick and tired of these ___undersexed suburban parents___ that think they can mistreat me. For the third time this week, somebody _confessed_ ___their clown fetish while grabbing my balloon animal___.
I'm done! Shove it.   Sincerely, ___Mr. Chuckles___

RIGHTEOUS
Resignations

ZOO KEEPER

Look, for years I've been one of the top _____
(profession)

_____ you've got. But I'm sick and tired of these

_____ that think they can
(main clientele/perpetrator of bad behavior)

mistreat me. For the third time this week, somebody

_____.
(bad behavior you're fed up with)

I'm done! Shove it.   Sincerely, _____
(profession-appropriate name)

MALL ELF AT CHRISTMAS

Look, for years I've been one of the top _____
(profession)

_____ you've got. But I'm sick and tired of these

_____ that think they can
(main clientele/perpetrator of bad behavior)

mistreat me. For the third time this week, somebody

_____.
(bad behavior you're fed up with)

I'm done! Shove it.   Sincerely, _____
(profession-appropriate name)

Please share your #RighteousResignationsPS   139

RIGHTEOUS
Resignations

DRIVER'S ED TEACHER

Look, for years I've been one of the top _____

(profession)

_____ you've got. But I'm sick and tired of these

_____ that think they can

(main clientele/perpetrator of bad behavior)

mistreat me. For the third time this week, somebody

_____.

(bad behavior you're fed up with)

I'm done! Shove it. Sincerely, _____

(profession-appropriate name)

INFLUENCER

Look, for years I've been one of the top _____

(profession)

_____ you've got. But I'm sick and tired of these

_____ that think they can

(main clientele/perpetrator of bad behavior)

mistreat me. For the third time this week, somebody

_____.

(bad behavior you're fed up with)

I'm done! Shove it. Sincerely, _____

(profession-appropriate name)

Please share your #RighteousResignationsPS

RIGHTEOUS
Resignations

MALE STRIPPER

Look, for years I've been one of the top _____
(profession)

_____ you've got. But I'm sick and tired of these

_____ that think they can
(main clientele/perpetrator of bad behavior)

mistreat me. For the third time this week, somebody

_____.
(bad behavior you're fed up with)

I'm done! Shove it.   Sincerely, _____
(profession-appropriate name)

SEPTIC TANK CLEANER

Look, for years I've been one of the top _____
(profession)

_____ you've got. But I'm sick and tired of these

_____ that think they can
(main clientele/perpetrator of bad behavior)

mistreat me. For the third time this week, somebody

_____.
(bad behavior you're fed up with)

I'm done! Shove it.   Sincerely, _____
(profession-appropriate name)

RAP INTERPRETATION

EXERCISE: You're a stuffy English teacher correcting and translating Classic Rap songs into proper English for this exercise. Of course, part of what makes rap music so great is the feel, attitude, and playfulness of language. So your job is to ruin it completely. Substitute these classic hip-hop lyrics whenever possible, with dry, literary dictionary terms. So you students can get a "C" in storytelling.

WHY?: Having to translate meaning, whether from one actual language to another or from a form of street slang to formal usage, makes us analyze words' meanings, inflections, and usage - to better understand social context and attitude. Language management is an excellent exercise to enhance creative awareness. As it calls upon attention _control,_ cognitive inhibition, and working memory to _reframe_ the story.

EXAMPLE:

FROM JUMP AROUND BY HOUSE OF PAIN
Word to your moms, I came to drop bombs
I got more rhymes than the Bible's got Psalms
And just like the Prodigal Son I've returned
Anyone stepping to me you'll get burned

THE TRANSLATION:
Please send a Linguistic element to your matriarchal figure, I arrived to release explosives. I possess a more significant number of resonating words than the Old Testament contains prayerful chants. Like the character from Luke 15:11, I came back. Each and every person who transgresses upon my space shall suffer high-temperature oxidation.

@creativityoncannabis

RAP INTERPRETATION

Translate these lyrics into formal speak:

FROM BABY'S GOT BACK BY SIR MIX A LOT

I like big butts and I can not lie
You other brothers can't deny
That when a girl walks in with an itty bitty waist
And a round thing in your face

TRANSLATION:

RAP INTERPRETATION

Translate these lyrics into formal speak:

FROM MS JACKSON BY THE OUTKAST

My baby's drama mama, don't like me
She be doing things like
Having them boys come from her neighborhood
To the studio trying to fight me
She need to get a, piece of the american pie and take her bite out
That's my house, I'll disconnect the cable and turn the lights out

TRANSLATION:

RAP INTERPRETATION

Translate these lyrics into formal speak:

FROM DEAR MAMA BY TUPAC

Now, ain't nobody tell us it was fair
No love from my daddy, 'cause the coward wasn't there
He passed away and I didn't cry, 'cause my anger
Wouldn't let me feel for a stranger
They say I'm wrong and I'm heartless, but all along
I was lookin' for a father, he was gone

TRANSLATION:

RAP INTERPRETATION

Translate these lyrics into formal speak:

FROM KING OF ROCK BY RUN DMC

I'm the king of rock, there is none higher
Sucker MC's should call me sire
To burn my kingdom, you must use fire
I won't stop rockin' till I retire

TRANSLATION:

DISCOVER YOUR
"Blues" Name

1. USE YOUR FIRST INITIAL TO FIND YOUR FIRST NAME...

A= Fat

B= Buddy

C= Sticky

D= Old

E=Texas

F= Hollerin'

G= Ugly

H= Brown

I= Happy

J= Boney

K= Curly

L= Pretty

M= Jailhouse

N= Peg Leg

O= Red

P= Sleepy

Q= Bald

R= Skinny

S= Blind

T= Big

U= Yella

V= Toothless

W= Screamin'

X= Fat Boy

Y= Washboard

Z= Steel-Eye

2. USE YOUR MIDDLE INITIAL TO FIND YOUR MIDDLE NAME...

A= Bones

B= Money

C= Harp

D= Legs

E= Eyes

F= Lemon

G= Killer

H= Hips

I= Lips

J= Fingers

K= Boy

L= Liver

M= Gumbo

N= Foot

O= Mama

P= Back

Q= Duke

R= Dog

S= Bad Boy

T= Baby

U= Chicken

V= Pickles

W= Sugar

X= Willy

Y= Tooth

Z= Smoke

3. USE YOUR LAST INITIAL TO FIND YOUR LAST NAME...

A= Jackson

B= McGee

C= Hopkins

D= Dupree

E= Green

F= Brown

G= Jones

H= Rivers

I= Malone

J= Washington

K= Smith

L= Parker

M= Lee

N= Thompkins

O= King

P= Bradley

Q= Hawkins

R= Jefferson

S= Davis

T= Franklin

U= White

V= Jenkins

W= Bailey

X= Johnson

Y= Blue

Z= Allison

Please share your #YourBluesNamePS

SLAPDASH SCREENPLAYS

EXERCISE: For this exercise, you're a screenwriter challenged to fix someone else's story. It happens all the time in Hollywood. There's an opening line and a theme for each act, but you need to put some ideas together quickly to save the project. You'll need to start your story with the given phrase and use the classic three-act format that all the studio execs expect - working the three given themes into each act.

THE SETUP: Inciting Incident, Call to adventure

THE CONFRONTATION: Roadblocks, Understanding the Challenges

THE RESOLUTION: Confrontation, Climax, Culmination

WHY?: Fiction is good for you. It stimulates the creative, logical, and emotionally connected parts of your brain, improving self-esteem and empathy. Following specific writing prompts forces your mind to be more conceptually elastic and puts your writing response into a sort of muscle memory. Organizational psychologist Adam Grant notes that expressive writing is linked to improved mood, well-being, and reduced stress levels for those who do it regularly.

SLAPDASH
Screenplays

ACT I: Pimple   **ACT II**: Turtles   **ACT III**: Lying

I hate wearing underwear...

SLAPDASH
Screenplays

ACT I: Rubbing   **ACT II**: Searching   **ACT III**: A Rabid Squirrel

I just finished writing a song...

Please share your #SlapdashScreenplayPS

SLAPDASH
Screenplays

ACT I: Sneakers   **ACT II**: Chess   **ACT III**: Helicopter

I will never forget that day...

SENSE STRETCHING

EXERCISE: Describe each of the items by employing senses that wouldn't normally be used. Describe the smell, color, taste, and sound (other than the sound of the word or the obvious sound the noun makes) you associate with each. You can work quickly and jot down the first responses that materialize in your head; or, feel free to sit with each phrase for a bit while your personal connections materialize. Everyone will process this task at a different speed.

WHY?: Synesthesia is a neurological phenomenon where the activation of one sense triggers an unrelated sense. Tasting music, for example, or hearing color. It's rare. But it's also eight times more common in writers and artists than in the population at large. Creativity is all about new approaches and surprising leaps. This activity draws on the concept by forcing you to explore unexpected sensory pathways and expanding your creativity in the process.

EXAMPLE:

	SMELL	**COLOR**	**TASTE**	**SOUND**
Falling in love	fresh laundry	midnight blue	applesauce	deafening hum
The word "fickle"	stale airplane air	pale green	tapioca pudding	distant traffic
Yoga	rubber	beige	pickled ginger	breezy treetops

@creativityoncannabis

SENSE STRETCHING

	SMELL	COLOR	TASTE	SOUND
Falling in Love				
The word "Fickle"				
Your current President				
Afternoon				
Sex				
Playing with Puppies				
Yoga				
Self-doubt				
Confidence				

Please share your #SenseStretchingPS

BRILLIANT IDEAS
I Had While Smoking Cannabis

BRILLIANT IDEAS
I Had While Smoking Cannabis

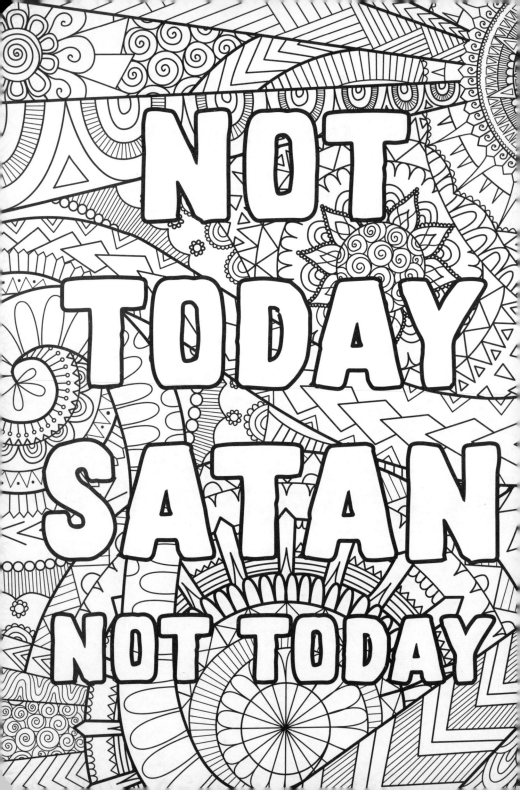

LAZY LOGIC

EXERCISE: Let's get inside the head of the laziest person you know - a spouse, kid, sibling, roommate, maybe you - why do they do (or not do) what they do? Choose a task that this person seems incapable of completing and then diagram their thought process with a workflow chart similar to the example. Begin with the often unaccomplished task and take various logical paths to complete it. Try to identify and empathize with their inner struggle. It can be as simple as unloading the dishwasher, mowing the lawn, lifting the toilet, or doing laundry. Share your findings with them for extra conflict!

WHY?: The act of role-playing provides a way to analyze and understand the perspective of others, while developing your skills of empathy and active listening. Empathy isn't easy - it takes creative awareness and a leap of imagination. Very often ad agencies will use this technique as a starting point in understanding how to influence their customers.

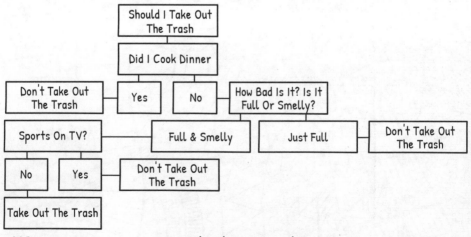

160

LAZY LOGIC FLOW CHART

LAZY LOGIC FLOW CHART

Please share your #LazyLogicPS

The man who has no imagination
has no wings.

– MUHAMMAD ALI,
Boxer, Activist, Entertainer, Poet

SO YOU WANT TO BE A TATTOO ARTIST

EXERCISE: Your job as the tattoo artist is to communicate through symbols. Imagine a person, real or ridiculous, and share their personal identity through a lower back tattoo. Remember, when it comes to tattoos, each has a story. They celebrate individuality and personality identity. You can look up tattoo symbol meanings for ideas and to help craft your story.

WHY?: Tattooing is one of humanity's most ancient forms of art. When a tattoo is designed, it is a unique piece of art created to make a statement or alter one's perceptions. Tattoo artists use empathy and creative awareness to represent a persons tribes, values, belief systems, and experiences.

EXAMPLE:

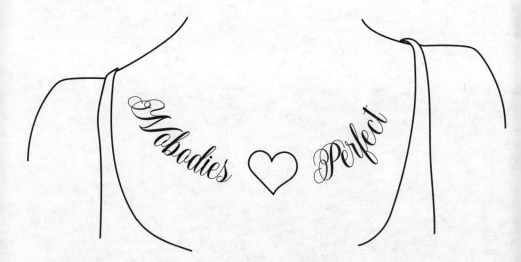

CREATE A TATTOO STORY

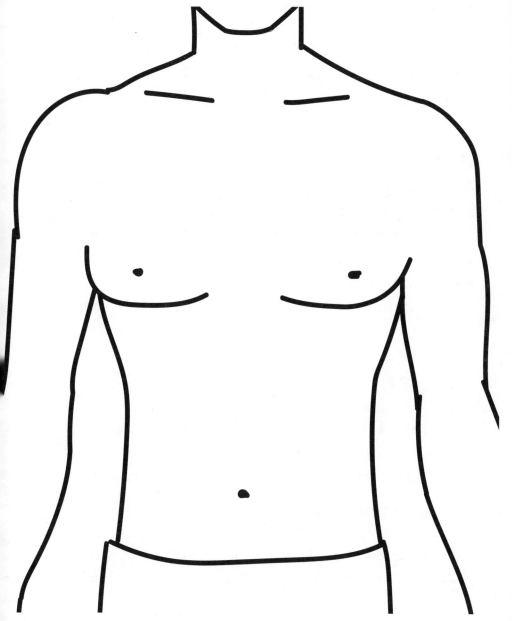

Please share your #TattooStoryPS

ABSURD SIMILARITIES

EXERCISE: A classic riddle from Lewis Carroll, author of Alice in Wonderland, asks: "How is a raven like a writing desk?" No one is sure, but it's puzzled readers and mad hatters for decades. In this exercise, flex your creative muscles to find similarities between very un-similar things - the stranger, the better!

WHY?: Einstein referred to this creative method as Combinatory Play, "The act of opening up one mental channel by dabbling in another." We often take for granted that certain things go together, and other things don't have anything in common. Identifying similarities between unrelated people, ideas of objects forces us to see them differently, stretching our imagination to find shared traits that might not have been obvious at first.

EXAMPLE:

HOW IS FREEDOM LIKE A DRY TOWEL?
- Both are needed for an enjoyable shower
- Absence of either one is a red flag for a terrible hotel

HOW ARE HOUSEPLANTS LIKE THE EIFFEL TOWER?
- I'm not qualified to take care of either one
- You can find fake versions of both at IKEA

ABSURD SIMILARITIES:

How is a deli sandwich like a hole in your sock?

How is the ocean like a passive aggressive compliment?

How is a wedding party like a corrupt lawyer?

How is glitter like a marriage?

How is self esteem like mowing the lawn?

How is The Queen of England like preschool show and tell?

DOODLES I DRAW DURING
Phone Calls & Important Meetings

You can't connect the dots
looking forward; you can only
connect them looking backwards.
So you have to trust that the
dots will somehow connect
in your future. You have to
trust in something – your gut,
destiny, life, karma, whatever.
This approach has never let me
down, and it has made all the
difference in my life.

– STEVE JOBS,
Founder Apple Computers

TWO KINDS OF PEOPLE

EXERCISE: Cat people and dog people. Folders and crumplers. Early birds and night owls. Spitters and swallowers. It's a binary world out there, folks! Consider each group listed and then fill in the blank with the "kind of people" that counters it. The approach is up to you. Your response can be silly or sage - your wisdom, your rules!.

WHY?: Social categorization happens when the brain groups together individuals to better understand them and the world they occupy. The process of grouping and the subsequent insights that come from "ordering" one's environment lead to heightened creative awareness. In this activity, the additional restrictions also trigger creativity by activating sensory perceptions and personal experiences to connect the topics to their "counter" categories.

EXAMPLE:

"There are two kinds of people...Those who never miss _Monday Night Football_ and those who never miss _2 pigeons fighting over a piece of bread_ ."

"There are two kinds of people...Those who are totally afraid of _ carbs _ and those who are totally afraid of _lettuce_ ."

@creativityoncannabis

TWO KINDS OF PEOPLE...

Those who always carry a _____ and those
who always carry a _____ .

Those who have fully memorized _____ and
those who have fully memorized _____ .

Those who were born with extra _____ and
those who were born with extra _____ .

Those who make you wanna go _____ and
those who make you wanna go _____ .

Those who you want on your side in a _____
and those you want on your side in a _____ .

Those whose nickname could be _____ and
those whose nickname could be _____ .

Those who win at _____ and those who
win at _____ .

TWO KINDS OF PEOPLE...

Those you can trust with your _____ and those you can trust with your _____ .

Those whose favorite app is _____ and those whose favorite app is _____ .

Those who only need 15 seconds to _____ a _____ and those who only need 15 seconds to _____ a _____ .

Those who are renowned for their amazing _____ _____ and those who are renowned for their amazing _____ .

Those who would rather die than _____ and those who would rather die than _____ .

Those who walk into a room and say, "_____ _____ " and those who say, "_____ _____ ".

Please share your #TwoKindsOfPeoplePS

I'd rather believe in my own choice and see it all go wrong than do something I'm not fully convinced of and later feel guilty about it.

– ALICIA KEYS,
Musician, Composer, Actress and Pianist

CREATIVE
REFLECTION

GUILTY PLEASURES

EXERCISE: You know those things you do in secret when you assume you're alone? Well, you weren't. Your great, great grandma's been with you the whole time. Write an apology letter to her ghost who has had to witness you be 100% unadulterated... You know what you did. That's why you have shivers running down your spine. Now say "sorry."

WHY?: They say you're only as sick as your secrets. According to Jack Goncalo, a professor of organizational behavior at Cornell University's School of Industrial and Labor Relations, people experience keeping a secret as a physical burden. Secrets literally weigh you down. But with a creative outlet, the burden of holding a big secret can be undone or mitigated.

EXAMPLE:

Dear Great Grandma Maye,
I just want to say I'm so embarrassed you saw me watching Keeping up With The Kardashians. I don't even like the show. It's just hard to stop watching, like a car crash. I mean, if the world ends and they wonder where it all went wrong, future archaeologist will be pointing to the first season of keeping up with Kardashians.
Again, sorry.

Love Jackie

LETTER TO GREAT,
Great Grandma

MY PERSONAL HELL

EXERCISE: Well, hell! You ended up in Hell. Let's call it... accidentally. You roll in with a good attitude, "Hey Satan, I've been told there was a special place for me down here!" But you soon realize that Hell isn't a generic one-size-fits-all deal, but instead, The Devil has done some deep market research and figured out that a more subtle, personalized approach is way more brutal. He's filling each person's Hell experience up with weird, random stuff that they always despised! Fill in the categories to describe your own personal Hell - the most annoying or loathsome things you can imagine.

WHY?: By engaging in examining your own personal hell, you're also bringing into focus its opposite - the wings that bring you joy, comfort, stimulation, fascination. And these are the things from which creation springs forth. It employs both a reflection-based brainstorming technique with the technique of changing your perspective so that you can look at the problem or situation from a completely different angle.

EXAMPLE: Martin's Personal Hell
What is served for every meal? **LIVER**
What song is on repeat? **TECHNO MUSIC**
What show/movie is on a loop on every TV? **GUNSMOKE RERUNS**
What job are you assigned? **CHEWED GUM FLOOR SCRAPER**
Who is your next-door neighbor? **ANYBODY NOSEY**
What's the weather? **FREEZING COLD**
What pet do you have? **SHIT-THROWING MONKEY**

@creativityoncannabis

ANSWER THESE QUESTIONS TO CREATE
Your Personal Hell

What is served for every meal?

What song is on repeat?

What show/movie is on a loop on every TV?

What job are you assigned?

Who is your next-door neighbor?

What kind of pet do you have?

What view outside your window?

What slogan is on your T-Shirt?

YOU ARE
WHAT YOU LOVE

EXERCISE: Who couldn't benefit from a bit of psychoanalysis. But who has the extra scratch for that when there are so many streaming services? But you're in luck! Respond to these four simple prompts, and several crucial aspects of your subconscious will be laid bare. Then, take a minute to reflect on which responses surprised you and which were spot-on. Share the test with friends.

WRITE DOWN YOUR ANSWERS ON THE OPPOSITE PAGE.
TURN TO PAGE 206 TO SEE WHAT THESE ANSWERS "REVEAL."

WHY?: This basic, four-question personality quiz was devised by psychoanalyst Carl Jung. He created tests like this one to see what's lurking underneath the ego. It's intended to reveal inner attitudes on essential matters. But keep in mind that it's simply a guide and that attitudes can changes. Understanding your attitudes and self-perceptions is a crucial tool in the building blocks of creativity.

SHARE YOUR ANSWER
& 3 adjectives about how it makes you feel

Name: _____

Favorite Color
  1.
  2.
  3.

Favorite Animal
  1.
  2.
  3.

Favorite Body Of Water
  1.
  2.
  3.

Imagine an empty white room. Take a minute to really picture yourself inside it - close your eyes if it helps. Share adjectives describing how it felt to be in that room.
  1.
  2.
  3.

SHARE YOUR ANSWER
& 3 adjectives about how it makes you feel

Name: _____

Favorite Color

1.

2.

3.

Favorite Animal

1.

2.

3.

Favorite Body Of Water

1.

2.

3.

Imagine an empty white room. Take a minute to really picture yourself inside it - close your eyes if it helps. Share adjectives describing how it felt to be in that room.

1.

2.

3.

Please share your #SelfPsychologyPS

SHARE YOUR ANSWER
& 3 adjectives about how it makes you feel

Name: _____

Favorite Color
1.
2.
3.

Favorite Animal
1.
2.
3.

Favorite Body Of Water
1.
2.
3.

Imagine an empty white room. Take a minute to really picture yourself inside it - close your eyes if it helps. Share adjectives describing how it felt to be in that room.
1.
2.
3.

MANUAL OF ME

EXERCISE: In this exercise, you'll explain how to care for a very complex organism - yourself! As any kid who's ever brought a hamster home from the pet store knows, new pets always come with a "Care & Keeping" guide, which tells you everything you need to know to keep that creature happy and healthy. What makes them feel safe? What kinds of treats do they like? What would someone need to know in order to keep you happy and well cared for? How should someone else interpret your behavior and understand your preferences and needs? Now do it for friends.

WHY?: Russian playwright Anton Chekhov said, "If you want to work on your art, work on your life." All the tools you need to make decisions, come up with ideas and be creative already exist in your head. It is just a problem of access. Stepping back and getting a better understanding of who you are and what you need to thrive makes it easier to build a foundation for creative innovation.

EXAMPLE:

THE CARE AND KEEPING OF: Zoo Breeze

INTRODUCTION: The Great North American Zoo Breeze is a social species who prefers the company of others. Intelligent and curious, Zoo Breeze enjoys meeting new people, and has little tolerance for boredom.

MOODS: You can tell when Zoo Breeze is in a happy mood if she is playing music loud and dancing around in her habitat. If Zoo Breeze is feeling low, she'll be quiet and stay on the sofa. Try cheering her up with a favorite song or sugary snack!

MANUAL OF ME

The Care and Keeping of:

Introduction:

Essential Equipment:

Moods:

Habitat:

Grooming:

Sleep habits:

Diet needs:

Favorite treats:

Likes:

Dislikes:

Play & Exercise:

MANUAL OF ME

The Care and Keeping of:

Introduction:

Essential Equipment:

Moods:

Habitat:

Grooming:

Sleep habits:

Diet needs:

Favorite treats:

Likes:

Play & Exercise:

Dislikes:

Please share your #ManualOfMePS

MANUAL OF ME

The Care and Keeping of:

Introduction:

Essential Equipment:

Moods:

Habitat:

Grooming:

Sleep habits:

Diet needs:

Favorite treats:

Likes:

Dislikes:

Play & Exercise:

FUNERAL MIXTAPE

EXERCISE: For obvious logistical reasons, you can't DJ your own funeral. But you can leave behind a mixtape for them to pop in the boombox! Make a mixtape of the top 5 songs you want played at your funeral. The songs can work together or each could serve a different purpose. You can tell your life story, reference specific folks in attendance, or just make people dance, laugh or cry. Whatever your approach, this is your chance to speak from the grave... using sweet tunes!

WHY?: Creating a mixtape or playlist demands a surprising array of thoughtful considerations - about audience, themes and sequence. Like any art, you're starting with scattered materials and shaping them into a dynamic, cohesive whole. And this particular exercise has extra significance: crafting the coda for your terrestrial existence. Are you looking for a grand celebration of you? Or will you send specific messages to individuals in attendance? That requires deep reflection... and some record spinning skills!

EXAMPLE:

> **SONG:** _"My Best Friend's Girl" The Cars_
>
> Why: A nod to my buddy's hot wife I flirted with
>
> Intended Reaction: An inside joke that will make her smile.

@creativityoncannabis

FUNERAL MIXTAPE

Name:

SONG:..
Why:
Intended Reaction:

SONG:..
Why:
Intended Reaction:

SONG:..
Why:
Intended Reaction:

SONG:..
Why:
Intended Reaction:

SONG:..
Why:
Intended Reaction:

FUNERAL MIXTAPE

Name:

SONG: ....

Why:

Intended Reaction:

SONG: ....

Why:

Intended Reaction:

SONG: ....

Why:

Intended Reaction:

SONG: ....

Why:

Intended Reaction:

SONG: ....

Why:

Intended Reaction:

Please share your #FuneralMixtapePS

FUNERAL MIXTAPE

Name:

SONG:..
Why:
Intended Reaction:

SONG:..
Why:
Intended Reaction:

SONG:..
Why:
Intended Reaction:

SONG:..
Why:
Intended Reaction:

SONG:..
Why:
Intended Reaction:

Please share your #FuneralMixtapePS

10 THINGS I CAN'T SAY OUT LOUD

1.

2.

3.

4.

5.

6.

7.

8.

9.

10.

WHAT DISTURBING FACT

Did This Tinder Date Just Reveal?
What are They thinking?

Please share your #StockPhotoSubtextPS

Above all, we are coming to understand that the arts incarnate the creativity of a free people.

- JOHN F. KENNEDY,
The 35th US President

THIS SONG SPEAKS TO ME

EXERCISE: You know how you hear a song, and it feels like it's speaking directly to you? Like when you're in love, or you just broke up with someone. For this exercise, we'd like you to literally respond to some songs. Go ahead and write a letter in response to the intent of these famous lyrics, as if the song is a letter to you. You can choose to respond to just specific lines that grab you. The tone of your letter can be annoyance, appreciation, confusion, or advice to the singer - it's up to you!

WHY?: Playing in imaginary worlds breeds practical creativity. Classic song lyrics are slices of poetry or even prose. Answering those lyrics can be seen as a form of 'fan fiction,' an activity that, research is showing, builds creative skills that pay off in real life. Fleshing out a universe demands creative imagination and attention to detail, consistency, rule sets, and logic. You have to grapple with constraints - just as when you're problem-solving at work.

THIS SONG SPEAKS TO ME
A Letter To Coldplay

Dear _____,
(your name)

It's such a shame for us to part. Nobody said it was easy.
No one ever said it would be this hard. Oh, take me back to the
start. I was just guessing at numbers and figures. Pulling the
puzzles apart. Questions of science, science and progress.

Sincerely,
Chris Martin
From "The Scientist"

Dear Chris,

Sincerely,

THIS SONG SPEAKS TO ME
A Letter To Drake

Dear _____,
(your name)

Hello? Yeah, I just walked in. Yeah, I'm good, you still working?
Tonight, right now? Did I go out? Yeah, I went out. I went,
I went to a couple of clubs. I never went to bed, shit,
wine or water. You said something about a cold drink?
I don't know, I'm delirious.

Sincerely,

Drake
From "Marvin's room"

Dear Drake,

Sincerely,

Please share your #ThisSongSpeaksToMePS

THIS SONG SPEAKS TO ME
A Letter To Prince

Dear _____ ,
(your name)
I guess I should've closed my eyes. When you drove me to the place where your horses run free. Cause I felt a little ill when I saw all the pictures of the jockeys that were there before me. Believe it or not, I started to worry. I wondered if I had enough class. But it was Saturday night, I guess that makes it all right. And you say "Baby, have you got enough gas?"

Sincerely,
Prince
"From LIttle Red Corvette"

Dear Prince,

Sincerely,

THE HOLIDAY LETTER

EXERCISE: The Holiday letter seems a bit unnecessary in the age of social media but not if you completely fabricate your life for entertainment purposes. For this exercise write a Holiday letter about all your experiences and achievements of the preceding year that shows how exceptionally fascinating you've become - or how you've totally lost your marbles.

SOME FARCICAL HOLIDAY LETTER TIPS:

- The achievements depicted should contain some connection to the truth, and personal flair, so that they know it's from you.

- Don't be afraid to brag or humble-brag. List fake job promotions, vacations you never took, and your children's accomplishments. You can also include the accomplishments of your pets or inanimate objects like your car.

- While you should use a personal touch, the ideas and traits should also be universal enough to be funny to a complete stranger

WHY?: From the beginnings of language humans have used stories to educate and entertain: myth, poetry, song, art, gossip, even politics. They are all forms of embellished storytelling. Nowadays, social media is a new way of telling stories. Creative storytelling engages the viewer with your content. It brings them into your world, and creates empathy and connection, even if it's a lie.

@creativityoncannabis

MY HOLIDAY
Letter

DOODLES I DRAW DURING
Phone Calls & Important Meetings

DOODLES I DRAW DURING
Phone Calls & Important Meetings

BRILLIANT IDEAS
I Had While Smoking Cannabis

BRILLIANT IDEAS
I Had While Smoking Cannabis

YOU ARE
WHAT YOU LOVE
Response Key (pg 180):

The color, animal, etc. you picked aren't the focus here - the descriptive words are.

1. Your "favorite color" adjectives represent how you view yourself.

2. Your "favorite animal" adjectives represent how you see other people.

3. Your "favorite body of water" adjectives represent your feelings about sex.

4. Your "white room" adjectives represent your feelings towards death.

Sweet, crazy conversations full
of half sentences, daydreams and
misunderstandings more thrilling than
understanding could ever be.

-TONI MORRISON,
Novelist, Essayist, College Professor

This is a test to see if your mission
in this life is complete, if you are
alive, it isn't.

– RICHARD BACH
Illusions: The Adventures of a Reluctant Messiah